A Teddy Horsle

The Grum|

Teddy Horsley learns about Forgiveness
Based on the Lord's Prayer

by Leslie J Francis and Nicola M Slee
Pictures by Laura Cooper

The Bear facts:

The Teddy Horsley Bible Series is designed to build bridges between the young child's day to day experiences of the world and major biblical themes and stories.

Both authors work in church-linked colleges concerned with Teacher Education. Nicola Slee lectures in Religious Studies at Whitelands College in London. Leslie Francis is Research Fellow at Trinity College in Carmarthen.

The Teddy Horsley Series is a result of both authors' extensive research into the religious development of young children and their wide experience of educational work in schools and churches.

Published by:
National Christian Education Council
1020 Bristol Road, Selly Oak
Birmingham, B29 6LB

British Library Cataloguing-in Publication Data:
A catalogue record for this book is available from the British Library.

Series editor: David Martin
Text © Leslie J Francis and Nicola M Slee 1990
Illustrations © National Christian Education Council 1994

Unless otherwise stated, quotations from the Bible are from the Good News Bible, published by the Bible Societies/Collins, © American Bible Society, New York, 1966, 1971, 1976.

First published 1989   Reprinted 1994
ISBN 0-7197-0841-9   Printed in England

It is Monday morning and Teddy Horsley is a grumpy bear.

Teddy Horsley wakes up early when Walter turns up his radio.

Walter says sorry, but Teddy Horsley throws his
pillow at him.

Teddy Horsley spills his drink when Betsy Bear bumps into the table.

Betsy Bear says sorry, but Teddy Horsley trips her up.

Teddy Horsley has to wait outside the bathroom when Lucy washes her hair.

Lucy says sorry, but Teddy Horsley bangs loudly on the door.

Teddy Horsley slips on the wet floor when Mrs Henry washes it.

Mrs Henry says sorry, but Teddy Horsley kicks her bucket.

Teddy Horsley falls over the cleaner when Mr Henry leaves it on the mat.

Mr Henry says sorry, but Teddy Horsley stamps his feet.

Teddy Horsley suddenly sees what a grumpy bear he is

and says sorry to Mr and Mrs Henry, Lucy,
Walter, and Betsy Bear.

Walter picks up the pillow and puts it on Teddy Horsley's bed.

Betsy Bear makes Teddy Horsley another drink and brings it to the table.

Lucy hurries in the bathroom and leaves it tidy for Teddy Horsley.

Mrs Henry dries the floor to make it safe.

Mr Henry puts the cleaner away in the cupboard.

Teddy Horsley knows that Mr and Mrs Henry,
Lucy, Walter, and Betsy Bear forgive him.

Teddy Horsley sees what a naughty bear he has been

and says sorry to God for being so grumpy.

Teddy Horsley knows that God forgives him too.

In *The Grumpy Day*, Teddy Horsley forgives Mr and Mrs Henry, Lucy, Walter, and Betsy Bear and receives forgiveness from them. He learns to say sorry to God and knows he receives God's forgiveness, too. These experiences bring alive Jesus' teaching to the disciples about how to pray in Matthew 6:

Jesus said, "This, then, is how you should pray . . .
'Forgive us the wrongs we have done,
as we forgive the wrongs that
others have done to us.'
Matthew 6. 9,12

The following questions suggest further ways of developing the links between the young child's experience, the story, and the Bible passage.

Talk about what makes you grumpy:
When do you get grumpy?
What makes you grumpy?
When do you say sorry?

Talk about the story:
What did Teddy Horsley do to Walter?
What did Teddy Horsley do to Betsy Bear?
What did Teddy Horsley do to Lucy?
What did Teddy Horsley do to Mrs Henry?
What did Teddy Horsley do to Mr Henry?
Why did Teddy Horsley say sorry to his family?
Why did Teddy Horsley say sorry to God?

Think some more about the story:
What other things might make Teddy Horsley grumpy?
What might he do?
How might he say sorry?

Think about the Bible passage:
What have you done today?
Who has made you grumpy?
How can you forgive them?
Who have you made unhappy today?
How can you say sorry to them?
How do people say sorry to God?

Titles in the series